# AWKWARD SILENCE

# AWKWARD SILENCE

## Practical Activities for White Ministry Leaders to Confront Anti-Racism

SHANI E. MCILWAIN

Special discounts are available on bulk quantity purchases by book clubs, associations and special interest groups. For details email: sales@publishyourgift.com or call (888) 949-6228.

For information log on to www.PublishYourGift.com

*Thank you to Mr. Gordon E. Houghtaling for being my first ally.*

*Dedicated to all of my white friends. I love you. Love bears all things, believes all things, hopes all things. Love never ends.*

*To all of my coaches past, present, and future, thank you for the opportunity to share space with you, help you, and pray with you along this journey. Remember, you are creative, resourceful, and whole. Godspeed.*

*For every Black body lost by hate. May your soul be at rest.*

*Inspired by life events, trauma, and triumphs.*

Letting go

**This anti-racism and anti-oppression work that we are committed to must have faithful leaders.**

Change is not going to happen overnight.
Embrace the small victories.

Celebrate them in community, and then keep going. One of the easiest things a person with privilege can do is bail out. When it gets hard and difficult, it is easy for white privilege to show up and do what is easy. We need you, as an ally, to stay at the table even when the table is destroyed.

We are doing the work of dismantling. One of the ways to do that is by going back to the beginning, and that beginning is your genesis story. This workbook is designed to get you to become familiar with your story in a way that you can't run from it—that even in its ugliness, it is there in front of you, and you don't default back to your familiar, but create a new familiar.

## Prayer

*Create in me a clean heart oh God,*

*that I may do the work I am called to do*

*and expected to do.*

*Amen.*

# TABLE OF CONTENTS

# COMMITMENT TO THIS WORK

**Why are you committed to doing this work?** This will be the fundamental question you will come back to over and over. Do not be superficial, do not give a textbook answer. I need your authentic, honest reason for your why.

**You** need your honest reason. If you cannot figure that out yet, then you are not ready to engage in this book or this work.

_____

_____

_____

_____

_____

_____

_____

_____

_____

_____

_____

_____

_____

*"People sometimes ask what advice I'd give to my younger self. I say, 'Start loving yourself today.' Knowing ourselves as beloved is where true life begins."*

—Rev. Bertram Johnson

# LET'S LEARN LANGUAGE AND DEFINITIONS

***What do these terms and phrases mean?*** This question is asked of me so many times, especially in my personal relationships with my white friends. Understanding language and phrases commonly used in this work will help us to more easily engage in these hard conversations over time. But one of the things I encourage people to do is be open to what the terms and definitions mean. Let Google guide you. The burden is not on Black people to teach you these things. It is always a blessing or a gift when Black people or other people of color decide to even engage in this conversation in the first place. So, when we take a proactive stance on this subject, it should always be received as a thank you.

Now, I will also say that I am always grateful when white people want to engage and learn as well, because in their privilege, they simply do not have to. This may not be a popular opinion, but it is mine. White people can ignore the injustices around them and live life to the fullest without a care or concern because privilege is not just tied to any socioeconomic construct but more built around options. Simply put, ya'll white people (I am writing this book for white people.) have more options in life simply because you are white. Now, I grew up in the poorest, most rural, whitest county in New York State, and all of my friends there will argue that they are not privileged. They will argue that they had to work just as hard as the next person—white, Black, immigrant, or otherwise. But, for me, the best way to describe what privilege looks like is in a story.

About seven years ago, when the word *privilege* began to make its way into my personal conversations with friends, my oldest friend did not see herself as a privileged person. She was a late-thirties, heterosexual, white woman who owned her own home and got great interest rates, but she did not see any of this as privilege. Me—knowing her story and often hearing about her childhood of growing up on food stamps and being reminded that I didn't—I never really had the language to explain what her privilege really looked like. So, because I am not a confrontational person with people I know, I chose to simply change the subject. Years later, my friend would call me to explain she understood what white privilege means. After another police shooting of an unarmed Black man, her son asked her if she ever prayed at night that he doesn't get shot by the police. She answered, *"No."* He said, *"Ma, that's privilege."*

Privilege for me is simply living without fear. Living without the fear that you will die because you are white. Even if you are the only white person in the room, you may be uncomfortable—but are you afraid? No one ever crosses the street because you are walking next to them on the sidewalk. No one clutches their bag as you make eye contact. No one follows you in a department store or puts you in handcuffs simply because you fit the description. All of these things I have experienced over and over throughout my life. I received "the talk" of what to do when stopped by police even in the early 1990s.

Black children are taught to call a lawyer when they are arrested. White children are taught to call their parents. This, my friends, is privilege at its very core. I am sure some other books will define privilege in a much more eloquent and academic way, but I teach by example and experience, so this is what you get.

Here are thirteen terms that you will need to know and understand when engaging in discussions of anti-racism and oppression:

1. **Allyship**. A lifelong learning from marginalized groups on how you can be supportive and assist with their needs. Allyship empowers said individuals or groups and also is an introspection into one's own self to see where your privilege and bias show up. Any and everyone can be an ally in some form. I have privilege being able bodied, heterosexual, and English being my first language.

2. **Anti-Racist**. If you have been engaged in this work for a while, then you may be familiar with a great resource, *How to Be an Antiracist* by Ibram X. Kendi. As Dr. Kendi defines this term, there is more to it than just saying you are not racist; you must be anti-racist, it is a set of beliefs and actions that oppose racism and promote the inclusion and equality of Black and brown people in society.

3. **BIPOC**. I am going to be completely honest with you. I learned this term maybe a year ago from a white ally. When I first heard it, I honestly thought it referred to bisexual people of color. So, if you thought that also, do an inhale/exhale right now. BIPOC refers to Black, Indigenous, People of Color. This term has become more popular in order to be more inclusive to all groups who have experiences with racism.

4. **Cisgender**. First thing we need to clear up is that sex and gender are two different things. Okay, so now that we have got that, cisgender means that one's gender matches their sex assigned at birth—e.g., I was born a female at birth. I identify as a female/woman. My pronouns are she/her.

5. **Critical Race Theory (CRT)**. Let's set the record straight for just a minute. This has been taught in United States education forever—well, maybe not forever but at least since 1982. But, all of a sudden it's a bad thing. Basically, CRT suggests that institutions and laws are constructed based on racism. And according to a study conducted by Purdue University, race isn't a biological reality but a social construct made by white people to maintain power. And furthermore, if I bring the scriptures into this definition, even the Bible does not separate people based on race but based on nation or ethnic group.

6. **Cultural Appropriation**. Cultural appropriation is defined as taking and exploiting one cultural expression in the form of art, music, or beauty standards without acknowledgment or regard of the culture it's been pirated from, and then getting accolades for it while the counter definition of cultural repercussions is passed down to the very people who essentially created the work, idea, or trend. For example, in the 2002 Eminem song "Without Me," he raps: *"I am the worst thing since Elvis Presley, To do black music so selfishly, And use it to get myself wealthy."*

7. **Emotional Labor**. The mental and unseen work that is required of BIPOC people each and every day is known as emotional labor. Writing this book was emotional labor for me.

8. **Emotional Tax**. This is the mental and unseen work that is required of BIPOC people to just feel included, valued, respected, and safe.

9. **Intersectionality**. This brings everything into the middle. And when I say everything, I mean everything. It is our personal stories, backgrounds, gender, ethnicity, social class, religion, sexual orientation—all of these things that result in a varied array of experiences, barriers, and opportunities.

| | |
|---|---|
| **10.** | **Reparations**. The act of repairing what has been broken, harmed, or damaged. Reparations is not new folks. We have been compensating people in the form of monetary damages since the New Testament. If someone hits your car, you take it in for repair and your car is fixed. Imagine if someone hit your car, left the scene, didn't admit fault, and you are stuck with the bill. How upset would you be that you would have to make yourself whole? |
| **11.** | **Unconscious Bias**. Basically, this is having a thought, generally a fleeting thought, that is connected to a stereotype of a particular group of people. |
| **12.** | **White Fragility**. Well, we see this quite often, but it's best described by my homegirl in my head, Robin DiAngelo, author of *White Fragility*, who defines this as *"a state in which even a minimum amount of racial stress becomes intolerable, triggering a range of defensive moves."* This played out for me, just in time to make the edits in this book.<br><br>A colleague sent me an email stating she wanted to have a conversation about a communication issue. I welcomed the conversation, and then she decided to have a meeting or, as she later said, *"just a call between friends."* When I suggested that the meeting without me was not fair and made me uncomfortable (I also said it was laced in white supremacist values and culture), she immediately left the conversation. DiAngelo concludes this definition as saying it is also *"the outward display of emotions such as anger, fear, and guilt, and behaviors such as argumentation, silence, and leaving the stress-inducing situation."* |
| **13.** | **White Privilege**. Having a set of advantages, opportunities, access, influence, simply because you are white. |

*"You were created to do extraordinary things.*

*Trust God and go forth!"*

—Ty Scott King

# UNDERSTANDING MICROAGGRESSIONS

Microaggressions. If I could define this as my mother would, it would be "saying dumb shit." But for the purpose of this book, I will clean it up and say microaggressions are indirect comments of racism, sexism, ableism, ageism, or another form of prejudice. Generally, when said, the person saying it doesn't even know it's offensive. But, it makes the other person feel different, devalued, unsafe, or violated. An example of a microaggression is saying to someone with an accent, *"Your English is very good. How long have you been in this country?"*

I was preaching for the first time at a church recently, and I overheard a congregant turn to her neighbor and say, *"She was really good, I didn't know she could speak so well."*

**If you are a white person reading this book and you do this— stop it!**

**If you are a white person who knows white people who do this—tell them to stop it!**

Here are just a few microaggressions that are often used without even knowledge of its harm or impact. Understanding that you have to unlearn long-held biases will be an ongoing and important part of your journey. Think of some other microaggressions you have used or heard and add them to the list.

1. Where are you from?

2. You don't act like a normal Black person.

3. So, like, what are you?

4. So what does your hair look like today?

5. You're not really Asian, are you?

6. I'm surprised you don't speak Spanish!

7. You are pretty, for a dark-skinned girl.

8. You are very well spoken. Your parents must be proud.

9. Why do you sound white?

10. Can I just call you _____ for short?

11.

12.

13.

14.

15.

16.

17.

18.

19.

20.

# THERE ARE FIVE THINGS THAT CAN HELP YOU AVOID MICROAGGRESSIONS IN EVERYDAY LIFE:

1. Be ready to learn.

2. Be ready to listen.

3. Do not get defensive or dismissive.

4. Hold yourself accountable.

5. Commit to changing your behavior.

In this section, we will complete a group exercise where we offer alternative language to help you avoid using microaggressions. The key is to be mindful of your words. If you have to think twice about saying something, my suggestion is *do not say it.*

| FREQUENT MICROAGGRESSION | ALTERNATIVE LANGUAGE |
|---|---|
| | |
| | |
| | |
| | |
| | |
| | |
| | |
| | |
| | |

*"If you're silent about your pain, they'll kill you and say you enjoyed it."*

—Zora Neal Hurston

# THE PROVEN PROCESS
# YIELDS RESULTS – PART I

When I am coaching groups and individuals, I am careful to express the fact that you should not be ashamed about being white. Please do not lament to me or anyone about this. We do not need your white guilt.

I need you to use your privilege like a superhero, I need you to use your opportunities, your influence, to fight the evils and injustices of racism. I see it done every day in healthy and organic ways. Even if it's a simple ask of a question in a meeting when deciding where to spend your money, who to hire for an event, where to shop, who to contract with, who your physician is, or how you make decisions because you have options that that many BIPOC people don't have, you can make a difference in small but impactful ways.

*"Some of us are called to keep showing up.*

*Some of us, not so much."*

—Sarang Kang

---

# [ S.H.A.R.E. ]

## SHARE YOUR STORY.

## HONESTY.

## ACCEPTANCE.

## RELATIONSHIP.

## EDUCATE.

---

It is my hope and prayer that this workbook will help you with tangible action items to being a better ally. It is not the end, however. There will always be a constant willingness to learn and evolve and learn again.

One of the things I enjoy doing is teaching with acronyms. Ever since I started writing books and preaching, my mantra has been "share." Share your story, share your testimony, share your feelings, just share. My weekly Facebook Live show is titled *"The Sharing with Shani Show."* My first book is titled *Sharing My Mess.*

I am a firm believer that sharing truth and vulnerability will help us transform and be better versions of ourselves. My five-step process is an ongoing rinse and repeat method, if you will.

## S     SHARE YOUR STORY

It was the fall of 1982. I was six years old, headed to the second grade, but my birthday was another three weeks away. My mother had moved us to live with her parents nearly three thousand miles away. See, I was born in Los Angeles, California. For the first seven years of my life, I had grown up as if my mother had worked at the United Nations. One of my oldest memories was a birthday party for a classmate named Shin. I played tag with Paola, Jamal, and Shin. Back in the 1970s and early 1980s, "we didn't see color." That would go on to become the most problematic teaching ever.

So on this sunny fall day in 1982, I boarded a school bus for the very first time, sat three rows behind the bus driver excited about the first day of school and excited about meeting new friends at a new school. I was about twenty minutes into the ride when the bus stopped at a white house with black shutters and four boys got on. One boy looked at me, smiled, and said, *"Oh look, a nigger is on the bus."* That was my first of many racist incidents. Every Black person remembers their incident. I was six years old. I was called nigger, African porch monkey, African booty scratcher. Find the worst, degrading, misogynistic slur possible and I heard it. And I heard it before I turned seven years old. Remember, this was 1982, not 1962.

This book was written with a necessary hesitation. Necessary because we are in the fight of our lives. Hesitation because of so many things. What will my white friends think of me being open and honest about race? What if I have to take an honest look at how my faith formation has played a role in the topics that I do not want to talk about? How can a writer who helps people get to a personal and intimate relationship with God talk about such a polarizing topic? I also hesitated with the idea of having to go back to traumatic situations I had buried deep down. I had to go back to my six-year-old self and remember that first day I heard the word nigger. I would have to go back to each and every racially charged encounter—when I was handcuffed and placed on the sidewalk with my children crying next me, when I got felt up by a state trooper at age nineteen and told I had "nice birthing thighs." These things and more would have to be revisited in order for me to give this book—this topic—any kind of breath. I am writing my story now because as I have been pushed into this work because of my faith and ministry work, I felt that perhaps my story, and the way in which I share the Good News, can somehow transform hearts, that perhaps a more academic, historical, statistical book can't do. So, if you are looking for data, proof of theory, or a whole bunch of footnotes and references from renowned sociologists, historians, and community activists, this is not the book. This book, and my hope for it, is simply to share my mess from the lens of being a Black woman, raising Black children, and praying daily that my Black son and daughters get home safe each and every day. This book, and my hope for it, is to simply share why it is important and necessary for white people—especially white Christians—to examine their hearts, do some relearning of what they thought they have already learned, and take that new knowledge and put it into tangible and actionable practices.

In this book, I will lean on the words of the people who I read, who I have learned from, who I have depended on when in my tears of anger, formed my language to speak what I have been trying to say for so long. When I am coaching faith leaders on anti-racism practices, I often start with a story. I am convinced that we overcome by the blood of the lamb and the power of our testimony (Rev. 12:11). It is the Bible, you know. When we share our stories, we begin to relate to each other in more ways than we think. Despite our different backgrounds, something in our stories is connected. Our stories also frame our whys. Why are you wanting to do this work? Why do you want to break down and dismantle institutional racism? Why do you want to work in building a beloved kin-dom? What is your why? How did you get here? Why are you drawn to social faith justice? Is social faith justice even a thing?

My story begins with my mother. If I am honest, I did not realize that my mother was an activist. She was also a feminist. I was born to a thirty-year-old, unwed (by choice)

Black woman, who never let a day go by to tell me that I was wanted. My mommy (yes, I called her Mommy well into adulthood) always told me, *"Shani, you were a planned pregnancy."* Over the years, I watched my mother advocate for children, mostly poor white children who were part of the Head Start program where she worked for years. Children with special abilities were her passion. I saw my mother take in domestic violence victims, move them to safe houses, babysit children when parents had to work, and so much more. But it was around 1984, when my mother was part of a grassroots campaign to get signatures of New York State voters to ratify the legislation of establishing a holiday in honor of Rev. Dr. Martin Luther King Jr., when I witnessed my mother advocating for Planned Parenthood because she said it helped get healthcare to poor women who would otherwise go without. My mother's story goes back to the Civil Rights Movement of the 1960s, the rise of Black Power in the 1970s. Remember, my mother did not have me until she was thirty, which in the 1960s was definitely uncommon. While her counterparts were getting married right after high school and having children, my mother, along with her friend, would be driving across the country one summer looking for Angela Davis when she was on the run.

My mother loved Jesus and would use scripture in a matter-of-fact, everyday language kind of way that when I heard it, I resonated with it. (Faith comes by hearing, right?) But never knew it was scripture until years later. And while Mommy loved Jesus, she loathed organized religion. The Church, she would say, was hypocritical. If there was anything I wish I could ask her now, it would be to say more about this Church hypocrisy, Mommy. Say more.

Even while she rejected the Church, my mother sent me to church. Every Sunday. I was very involved in church. As I have said before, I knew Jesus. I prayed to Jesus. I accepted Jesus as Lord and Savior at four years old and confirmed my faith at twelve. But it wasn't until age thirty-three when I realized I had no relationship with Jesus at all. Say more about this hypocrisy, Mommy.

One thing to point out as we begin this work is this: My having been raised in an all-white small town definitely formed me and my views on race, the Church, and community—in good ways and bad. I had a good childhood. I have amazing friends who are considered family. And, while I know that for some of my "family," this book may be hard to read, it is necessary. It's going to be a relearning of me, a relearning of what you think was, and a relearning of what should be now. My hope and prayer is that while there will be tension, we find some healing and movement on the other side.

The time is now. The time is right now. Racism and white supremacy cannot be dismantled without people. All people. We need each other to do this work. The time is right now.

It is now time to share your story. When was the first time you were aware of different races? Who was the first person you met that was not the same racial or ethnic group as you?

**Share your story here:**

_____

_____

_____

_____

_____

_____

_____

_____

_____

_____

_____

_____

_____

_____

_____

_____

## H HONESTY

If I am being honest, I avoided writing this book for many years out of fear.

If I am being transparent, it was out of fear of being rejected by my white friends.

I could probably count on one hand—hell, one finger—how many times since I was six years old that we talked about race. Honestly, the older I have gotten, the more I have realized my silence was rooted in having these hard truths and having to explain myself in a way that I had never done before, making me vulnerable. I worried that my friends, my sisters, would say something or believe something so outrageous that we could not recover. I did not want our relationship to change in a negative way. But love has a way of making things right.

We have to believe that love hopes all things, believes all things, and love never dies. It is with a profound love for my friends, for humanity, for God that I share my deepest feelings.

**Take an honest assessment of yourself. Examine your heart. What do you need to be honest about?**

_____

_____

_____

_____

_____

_____

_____

_____

_____

_____

_____

_____

_____

_____

_____

_____

_____

_____

## A — ACCEPTANCE

Accepting the fact that there will be successes and failures in the ongoing work of anti-racism will help you when failures come. One of my biggest failures of being an ally is when I was having dinner with a few literary executives. During dinner, I referred to a same-sex relationship as a "lifestyle," which offended the gay man at the table. As he began to express his deep offense to my comment, I began to take it personally. I was reciting comments in my head, formulating my defense, getting ready to justify my words. But instead, I counted to ten and remembered my allyship training: *Intention means nothing when it comes to impact.* I did not intend to do harm, but the impact of my words did. So, I began to listen. I apologized and I listened.

I wish I could end the story there, but no, I can't. Ego set in, and days later, I contacted all of my LGBTQIA+ friends to ask their opinion. All of them said they were not offended. But I finally had one friend who spoke truth to power. She said, while she wasn't offended, it did not matter—my colleague was, and that's really all that matters.

We must remember that each case of offending or failing is unique. It does not matter if your Black friend, Asian friend, or whomever did not find what you said to be a microaggression or harmful; the person who you offended has a right to feel what they feel. Accept the critique and vow to do better. Period.

**What are some things you need to accept about this work and about yourself? This list goes to twenty, but to get started, give me at least five.**

1. _____
2. _____
3. _____
4. _____
5. _____
6. _____
7. _____
8. _____
9. _____
10. _____
11. _____
12. _____
13. _____
14. _____
15. _____
16. _____
17. _____
18. _____
19. _____
20. _____

Two years before Trayvon Martin was murdered, I received a phone call from an unknown caller. I usually do not answer those calls, but I did that day. On the other end of the phone was my almost fourteen-year-old son, frantic. He had been detained by the Washington Metropolitan Transit Authority Police department (WMATA). WMATA officers have essentially the same power as a regular police officer, but their jurisdiction is at metro stations and a five-mile radius within a station. On this particular day, a six-foot-three-inch tall, light-skinned Black man between the ages of twenty-five and thirty, wearing all black clothing, and long dreadlocks, was accused of fare aversion. My son, along with his best friend, were freshmen in high school wearing red school uniform shirts and khaki pants. They were stopped at the station and detained because they "fit the description." Even wearing their school shirts, even the fact that all DC school-aged kids can ride the metro train and bus for free, they were detained. Even with them being at least ten years younger than the alleged suspect, they were detained.

I rushed to the station with a birth certificate in hand, worried that would not be good enough. I worried because my son at thirteen and seven months old was already six feet tall. But he was still a kid, just a tall skinny boy who was scared but did not want to show it. When I got there, I did not show the birth certificate. The officer said, "You can go." I asked, "What can I do as his mother to avoid this from happening again?" The officer, a white man, sized me up and said flippantly, "Get an ID." So, the next day I went into work late, and went to the DC Department of Motor Vehicles to get my thirteen-year-old a non-driver's identification card. Since we were there early, I remember waiting only about twenty minutes before our number was called, only to be turned away. In DC, you cannot get a non-driver's identification card until you are fifteen years old. I spent the next year and five months with a knot in my throat. Every time Roderick left the house, I worried what the next call would sound like simply because he fit the description.

I share this story under relationships because of the impact it has had when telling my stories. I have cultivated authentic relationships with people that my children now become extensions of those relationships. So when you see an injustice done to another fifteen-year-old Black boy, you think of my child or the child of your friend. Relationships create empathy. Empathy creates compassion. Compassion creates action. Action changes lives.

Do you have authentic relationships both personally or as a collective group? Are you looking to create a new relationship with another church or group?

*"Belonging is being loved and cared for—even when you're at capacity and your reserves are depleted. Belonging is being seen and heard—even when you are operating in the shadows and have nothing left to say."*

—Katherine Lee Baker

## E  EDUCATE

Let's discuss the term "you people" or "you better tell your people."

More often than not, someone will slide in my inbox and make these authoritative statements in an attempt to assert their whiteness. This recently happened after a Black man was caught on camera brutally attacking an elderly Asian American and Pacific Islander (AAPI) woman. It was senseless and utterly wrong. There are much more qualified sociologists and psychologists who can break down how white supremacy is designed to keep marginalized communities separated and against each other. Nevertheless, telling someone "you people" or "you better tell your people" is very problematic and racist on so many levels. Black people are not monolithic. We do not all think alike. But, rest assured, we do not condone violence against AAPI or any other ethnic group.

The difference between saying, "White people need to talk to white people," and that of the prior statement is that the system in which white people benefit from is set up to protect white people from their bad behavior. There is no system that protects Black people. AAPI hate crime bills are passed in Congress with bipartisan support, yet an anti-lynching bill still sits in Congress stalemated since 2019. This country will need to reconcile with itself and its history of Black people before we can see progress that is continual.

Educating ourselves and giving space to unlearn and relearn will help us move forward. It will help us be better allies and, even better, children of God.

**Where are some areas that you need to educate yourself? Why?**

_____

_____

_____

_____

_____

_____

_____

_____

_____

_____

_____

_____

_____

_____

_____

_____

_____

# THE PROVEN PROCESS YIELDS RESULTS – PART II

In the next section, we are going to do a deep dive into thirteen White Supremacy Culture Characteristics that must be deconstructed and dismantled in order for real process and change to occur. Using another form of the S.H.A.R.E. process, I have changed some of the words in order to offer more practical and substantial productivity with our exercises. And, because this workbook is for faith leaders, it is time to either get your Bible or pull up the app on your phone.

1. Find a **Scripture** that releases you from the characteristic.

2. Be **Honest** in why this characteristic is something you hold onto.

3. Determine who will hold you **Accountable** when this characteristic appears.

4. List the steps you will take to **Relearn** and **Repair**.

5. **Exercise** what you have learned. Put the newfound awareness into practice. Write down how you will do this.

> *"Always listen with empty ears."*
>
> —Amantha

# WHITE SUPREMACY CHARACTERISTICS

In their web-based workbook for *Dismantling Racism Works (dRworks)*, Kenneth Jones and Tema Okun of ChangeWork 2001 provide thirteen attributes of white supremacy culture. Along with the below, we will list even more characteristics to get a fuller picture of how White Supremacy is rooted in everything we do. It is the air we breathe.

| | |
|---|---|
| **1. Perfectionism** | little appreciation expressed among people for the work that others are doing; appreciation that is expressed usually directed to those who get most of the credit anyway |
| **2. Sense of Urgency** | continued sense of urgency that makes it difficult to take time to be inclusive, encourage democratic and/or thoughtful decision-making, to think long-term, to consider consequences |
| **3. Defensiveness** | the organizational structure is set up and much energy spent trying to prevent abuse and protect power as it exists rather than to facilitate the best out of each person or to clarify who has power and how they are expected to use it |

| | |
|---|---|
| **4. Quantity Over Quality** | all resources of organization are directed toward producing measurable goals; things that can be measured are more highly valued than things that cannot, for example, numbers of people attending a meeting, newsletter circulation, and money spent are valued more than quality of relationships, democratic decision-making, and the ability to constructively deal with conflict; little or no value attached to process; if it can't be measured, it has no value; discomfort with emotion and feelings; no understanding that when there is a conflict between content (the agenda of the meeting) and process (people[s] need to be heard or engaged), process will prevail (for example, you may get through the agenda, but if you haven't paid attention to people[s] need to be heard, the decisions made at the meeting are undermined and/or disregarded |
| **5. Worship of the Written Word** | if it's not in a memo, it doesn't exist; the organization does not take into account or value other ways in which information gets shared |
| **6. Paternalism** | decision-making is clear to those with power and unclear to those without it; those with power think they are capable of making decisions for and in the interests of those without power |
| **7. Either/Or Thinking** | things are either/or, good/bad, right/wrong, with us/against us; closely linked to perfectionism in making it difficult to learn from mistakes or accommodate conflict; no sense that things can be both/and |

| | |
|---|---|
| **8. Power Hoarding** | little, if any, value around sharing power; power seen as limited, only so much to go around |
| **9. Fear of Open Conflict** | people in power are scared of conflict and try to ignore it or run from it; when someone raises an issue that causes discomfort, the response is to blame the person for raising the issue rather than to look at the issue which is actually causing the problem; emphasis on being polite; equating the raising of difficult issues with being impolite, rude, or out of line |
| **10. Individualism** | little experience or comfort working as part of a team; people in organization believe they are responsible for solving problems alone; accountability, if any, goes up and down, not sideways to peers or to those the organization is set up to serve; desire for individual recognition and credit; leads to isolation |
| **11. Progress Is Bigger, More** | observed in systems of accountability and ways we determine success; progress is an organization which expands (adds staff, adds projects) or develops the ability to serve more people (regardless of how well they are serving them); gives no value, not even negative value, to its cost, for example, increased accountability to funders as the budget grows, ways in which those we serve may be exploited, excluded, or underserved as we focus on how many we are serving instead of quality of service or values created by the ways in which we serve |

**12. Objectivity**

the belief that there is such a thing as being objective; the belief that emotions are inherently destructive, irrational, and should not play a role in decision-making or group process; invalidating people who show emotion; requiring people to think in a linear fashion and ignoring or invalidating those who think in other ways; impatience with any thinking that does not appear "logical" to those with power

**13. Right to Comfort**

the belief that those with power have a right to emotional and psychological comfort (another aspect of valuing "logic" over emotion); scapegoating those who cause discomfort; equating individual acts of unfairness against white people with systemic racism which daily targets people of color

**What are other characteristics and attributes that you show up first within yourself and then second in your context?**

*"You can trick your mind,
if you change your words."*

—Mika Fresh

# [ S.H.A.R.E. ]
# SCRIPTURE.
# HONEST.
# ACCOUNTABLE.
# RELEARN. REPAIR.
# EXERCISE.

Using this five-step S.H.A.R.E formula, we are going to dismantle these White Supremacy Characteristics. I want you to think first about yourself. More often than I can count, my clients and coaches do not like doing inner work when it comes to dismantling systemic racism and oppressed systems. I believe that dismantling starts from within. Romans 12:2 reminds us that transformation begins with a renewing of the mind, but I will add that the **heart** must be transformed before the mind can even open up to the possibility of something new.

As a reminder, we are going to deconstruct each characteristic using these steps:

1. Find a **Scripture** that releases you from the characteristic.

2. Be **Honest** in why this characteristic is something you hold onto.

3. Determine who will hold you **Accountable** when this characteristic appears.

4. List the steps you will take to **Relearn** and **Repair**.

5. **Exrercise** what you have learned. Put the newfound awareness into practice. Write down how you will do this.

We will break down the S. H. A. R. E. formula for each of the characteristics below.

## 1) Perfectionism

Scripture: _____

Honesty: _____

Accountability: _____

Relearn/Repair: _____

Exercise: _____

## 2) Sense of Urgency

Scripture: _____

Honesty: _____

Accountability: _____

Relearn/Repair: _____

Exercise: _____

## 3) Defensiveness

Scripture: _____

Honesty: _____

Accountability: _____

Relearn/Repair: _____

Exercise: _____

## 4) Quantity Over Quality

Scripture: _____

Honesty: _____

Accountability: _____

Relearn/Repair: _____

Exercise: _____

## 5) Worship of the Written Word

Scripture: _____

Honesty: _____

Accountability: _____

Relearn/Repair: _____

Exercise: _____

## 6) Paternalism

Scripture: _____

Honesty: _____

Accountability: _____

Relearn/Repair: _____

Exercise: _____

## 7) Either/Or Thinking

Scripture: _____

Honesty: _____

Accountability: _____

Relearn/Repair: _____

Exercise: _____

## 8) Power Hoarding

Scripture: _____

Honesty: _____

Accountability: _____

Relearn/Repair: _____

Exercise: _____

## 9) Fear of Open Conflict

Scripture: _____

Honesty: _____

Accountability: _____

Relearn/Repair: _____

Exercise: _____

## 10) Individualism

Scripture: _____

Honesty: _____

Accountability: _____

Relearn/Repair: _____

Exercise: _____

## 11) Progress is Bigger, More

Scripture: _____

Honesty: _____

Accountability: _____

Relearn/Repair: _____

Exercise: _____

## 12) Objectivity

Scripture: _____

Honesty: _____

Accountability: _____

Relearn/Repair: _____

Exercise: _____

## 13) Right to Comfort

Scripture: _____

Honesty: _____

Accountability: _____

Relearn/Repair: _____

Exercise: _____

# INDIVIDUAL WORK

RELAX—you did it! You leaned into the vulnerable spaces of your heart and soul. This is amazing. Now, let's do this activity with the top three characteristics that you added at the beginning of this exercise. For instance, for me, I would add "Professionalism."

**1)** _____

    Scripture: _____

    Honesty: _____

    Accountability: _____

    Relearn/Repair: _____

    Exercise: _____

**2)** _____

    Scripture: _____

    Honesty: _____

    Accountability: _____

    Relearn/Repair: _____

    Exercise: _____

**3)** _____

Scripture: _____

Honesty: _____

Accountability: _____

Relearn/Repair: _____

Exercise: _____

# CONTEXT WORK

How do these characteristics show up in your church or organizational context? We will do this same exercise again, this time focusing on the institution.

## 1) Perfectionism

Scripture: _____

Honesty: _____

Accountability: _____

Relearn/Repair: _____

Exercise: _____

## 2) Sense of Urgency

Scripture: _____

Honesty: _____

Accountability: _____

Relearn/Repair: _____

Exercise: _____

## 3) Defensiveness

Scripture: _____

Honesty: _____

Accountability: _____

Relearn/Repair: _____

Exercise: _____


## 4) Quantity Over Quality

Scripture: _____

Honesty: _____

Accountability: _____

Relearn/Repair: _____

Exercise: _____


## 5) Worship of the Written Word

Scripture: _____

Honesty: _____

Accountability: _____

Relearn/Repair: _____

Exercise: _____

## 6) Paternalism

Scripture: _____

Honesty: _____

Accountability: _____

Relearn/Repair: _____

Exercise: _____

## 7) Either/Or Thinking

Scripture: _____

Honesty: _____

Accountability: _____

Relearn/Repair: _____

Exercise: _____

## 8) Power Hoarding

Scripture: _____

Honesty: _____

Accountability: _____

Relearn/Repair: _____

Exercise: _____

## 9) Fear of Open Conflict

Scripture: _____

Honesty: _____

Accountability: _____

Relearn/Repair: _____

Exercise: _____

## 10) Individualism

Scripture: _____

Honesty: _____

Accountability: _____

Relearn/Repair: _____

Exercise: _____

## 11) Progress is Bigger, More

Scripture: _____

Honesty: _____

Accountability: _____

Relearn/Repair: _____

Exercise: _____

## 12) Objectivity

Scripture: _____

Honesty: _____

Accountability: _____

Relearn/Repair: _____

Exercise: _____


## 13) Right of Comfort

Scripture: _____

Honesty: _____

Accountability: _____

Relearn/Repair: _____

Exercise: _____

*The world does not need white people to civilize others. The real White People's Burden is to civilize ourselves."*

—Robert Jensen

# WHY ARE YOU HERE?

Many clients I have worked with may have already started their journey in allyship. They may have completed allyship training, read one of the many books on current booklists (*Dear White Christians*, *White Fragility*, etc.), but they are still unsure of how to take action. They come to me because their biggest question is, "Now what?"

If my clients are in this "now what?" phase, I always tell them to start small. First, we identify *why* they read those books and *why* they think they need additional help in practicing anti-racism and allyship. During sessions, the first question I always ask is, *"Why are you here?"* This usually results in an awkward silence. Even though it seems like a simple question, this is the baseline for doing anti-racism work. Asking yourself this question can open your mind in new ways and bring about more intentional action. The answer could be something as big as "I just want to make this world better for my child" or "I know this is what my purpose is." But we have to get to the why. And however long that takes—three months, six months, your entire life—that is how long you must do the work. You must constantly go back to that "why" because if you are unsure of the why, you are going to lose your footing too quickly and want to give up.

Once the why is defined, I ask that you identify just one goal and write it down. Though many people I work with want to solve all of life's problems at one time, it is important to focus on just one goal at a time. Remember, slavery lasted for four hundred years. We are not going to fix or dismantle any type of racial problems and get to racial equity overnight, right? It is not going to happen overnight. Because we, especially high achievers, are so prone to wanting to find solutions to problems quickly, we have the tendency to read books or sign up for training sessions and feel like we need to solve the problem right away. But it doesn't work like that. These social issues have been ingrained in our society for so long, it is going to take time and will require constant reflection on your intentions to move forward and enact change effectively.

Like me, many of my clients face the obstacle of fear. They have a fear of failing, a fear of taking the wrong step, which causes them to overanalyze their decisions and hesitate in taking action. Because now that they are aware, the next puzzle to solve is how to apply this knowledge they have gained, and not just to their professional contexts of being in ministry, but personally. Many leaders in ministry think they need to have all the necessary tools before starting this work. There is this need for perfection, this need to get everything right and not make mistakes. But you must realize that you are going to make mistakes. You are going to say the wrong thing to a BIPOC person. It is just inevitable, and you can learn from those experiences.

It is important to know that you will never reach a point where your work is done. The work of an ally never stops. Allyship is a lifelong process—a lifelong process in which people with privilege and power work to develop empathy toward other marginalized groups' challenges and their issues. Even if you have done the work within yourself, many of you will still have to navigate friends and family who have opposing views and may not be prepared to have those conversations. Taking what you have learned and applying it to help others is a whole other step.

Being an ally requires constant learning and unlearning, falling and getting back up. It is just like discipleship. The two go hand in hand. So, if you think you have mastered discipleship, then you are wrong about that too. And what allyship and anti-racism look like today may change in six months from now—because the world changes. In 2019, we had not yet experienced the global pandemic that began in 2020. The pandemic alone pointed out many issues of how systemic racism has played a part in trying to eradicate a virus. There is always going to be something that is going to cause us to turn our attention to that one thing and to work on that. Just as "love" is an action word, so are "allyship" and "anti-racism."

# HEART CHARACTERISTICS

In this section, we will take a heart check assessment of who you are. Who is showing up in the world each day? How do you see yourself?

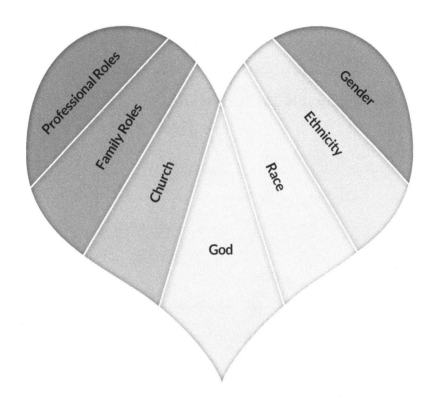

Using the heart characteristics found in the picture above, list them in order of importance for you, describe each one, and why that specific characteristic holds importance.

**1.** _____

**Describe your role and why it holds importance for you.**

_____

_____

_____

_____

**2.** _____

**Describe your role and why it holds importance for you?**

_____

_____

_____

_____

**3.** _____

**Describe your role and why it holds importance for you?**

_____

_____

_____

_____

**4.** _____

**Describe your role and why it holds importance for you?**

_____

_____

_____

_____

**5.** _____

**Describe your role and why it holds importance for you?**

_____

_____

_____

_____

**6.** _____

**Describe your role and why it holds importance for you?**

_____

_____

_____

_____

**7.** _____

**Describe your role and why it holds importance for you?**

_____

_____

_____

_____

# YOUR JOURNEY IN ANTI-RACISM WORK

In completing your anti-racism work, it is important to truly understand that your mind cannot change until an experience has had a direct effect on your heart and on your soul. It is my hope for you, as Christians, that you feel the same heart transformation as a result of this anti-racism work that you experienced when you allowed Jesus into your heart. You may already know in your head that what you are witnessing is wrong, but your heart has to go through that transformation.

As privileged people, you can wake up one day and decide that you do not have to deal with the injustices of your communities and society as a whole. You can make a conscious decision to not deal with any of it. But when you go through a heart transformation, or an attack of the heart, when you see something that you cannot unsee, when you see a modern-day lynching, when you see a man begging for his life as another man's knee is pressed on his neck, and you cannot get that image out of your head, you cannot sleep at night, and you are angry beyond measure—*that* is a change in your heart. You have reached that point of righteous anger, that point of transformation in your soul.

If you are a faith-based leader or congregation member who is ready to take the next step in your anti-racism and allyship practice, the following three key messages will help you as you begin your journey.

## 1) Failing is a part of your success.
The first major key to allyship is recognizing and believing that it is okay to fail. It is okay to make a mistake. It is okay that you are not going to always get it right. Acknowledging that you made or will make a mistake, acknowledging that you could have done or can

do something differently next time, and getting back up is what will help you succeed time and time again. The more you get back up, the less you are going to fall again. Be okay with failing and use each failure as a guide for moving forward.

**Describe a time when you failed in your allyship or privilege.**

_____

_____

_____

_____

**What did you learn?**

_____

_____

_____

_____

**What will you differently next time?**

_____

_____

_____

_____

## 2) You already have the power to influence change.

What is your power? Recognize what power you have already within the system and use your power for good. Though you may not recognize this now, you already have the necessary tools and resources at your disposal to begin this work. Use what you have and build from there; find the niche you have already built as a faith leader, as a congregation. Your niche could be working in immigration, working in restoring and repairing your community, offering reparations—it can be anything. I realized my gift lies in sharing my story. I realized that when I shared my experiences, I was able to build a relationship with people, and they were able to feel compassion. These relationships make an impact, and each of you has a unique way of forming these connections and inspiring others to do better, to do good.

**Write down 5 ways you can use you power and privilege to enact change?**

| POWER | PRIVILEGE |
|---|---|
|  |  |
|  |  |
|  |  |
|  |  |
|  |  |

**How can your institution use its power to enact change?**

| INSTITUTIONAL POWER | ACTION ITEM TO CREATE EQUITY |
|---|---|
|  |  |
|  |  |
|  |  |
|  |  |
|  |  |

### 3) Keep learning and relearning.

You will never be an expert. Once you realize that, you will live into a posture of humility. It is completely up to you to continue to learn and grow and push yourself out of your comfort zone. Do not settle for your comfort. Sit in the tension. Learn how to speak when you need to speak and be quiet when you need to be quiet. But, most importantly, listen to God. What is the Holy Spirit prompting you to do in this moment? Right now. Write it down.

# CONCLUSION

The more I work in the anti-racism and oppression circle, I am convinced of one thing. This is heart work. This entire Christian journey has been a transformative heart work experience. Every single human condition—good or bad—must be connected back to the heart. If the heart does not want to be compassionate and restorative, then it does not matter how many workshops, conferences, bible studies, books, podcasts, coaching cohorts, and mandated required training you can check off—you will not be transformed. The deep parts of the heart that we try to keep away from God.

The parts of the heart we hate to expose because if we did, we wouldn't know how to explain those feelings. Our personal relationship with God should be based on truth. Truth opens us up to intimacy, and through this intimate relationship, we can allow God to transform us from the inside out. We can grab hold of the courage that is one of God's promises for us.

You are almost finished!

If you are tired of sharing your feelings, thoughts, and stories, then I have done my job. **Silence is violence.** The interaction that has taken place during this course is to encourage and equip you to use your voice. It is time to use your privilege. It is time for the awkwardness of your silence to end. It is time to get rid of whatever hindrance you have and be leaders.

Be leaders of your church, your communities, your families. It is time to share your story and be the light that God has called you to be.

For additional resources and tools, go to
**www.awkwardsilencebook.com**

For group and individual coaching,
contact **info@shanimcilwain.com**

For speaking and tour schedule,
**www.shanimcilwain.com**

- shani
- mary Joe → gray hair
- Julie (pastor) → blue sweate
- Laura w/ dog —

# SPECIAL THANKS AND ACKNOWLEDGMENTS

Thanks for holding me accountable, prayers, concerns, and all that good, good stuff...

*Roderick, Raianna, Michayla, and Elisia*: you will always be the reason why. You will always be inspiration for me. I am because of you. You can because of all who came before you. I love you!

*Tie*, we made another one! I am forever grateful for just sharing space with you, learning from you, growing with you. Thank you for seeing my vision and making it a reality. Thank you for being more than my publisher, thank you for loving me like a sister, and being my friend.

*Bryan*, I know you didn't want a special shout out in this book, but I wrote this book at the exact time we met, grew our friendship, and cultivated a partnership. When I wanted to quit, you wouldn't let me, and for that I am grateful. Thank you for your support, your love, every shared post, every late-night motivational speech, and most importantly, thank you for being you.

*My crew*, Heather, Nicole C., Ronnie, Jerrica, Vita, Melonise, Nicole B., Veronica, Kae, Tara Spuhler McCabe, Jen James, Jessica Tate, Casey Wait, Jesy Littlejohn, LeAnn Hodges, MaryAnn McKibben Dana, Blair Moorhead, and Nancy Neal

*My NEXT Friends*, Bertram Johnson, Amantha Barbee, John Wilkinson, Meghan Gage Finn, Susan Thornton, Suzanne Davis, Adam Fronczek, Glenn McCray, Adriene Thorne, Christopher Holland, Sara Dingman, Christopher Dela Cruz, Tanner Pickett, Lisle

Gwynn Garrity, Steve Lindsley, Sarang Kang, Carlton Johnson, Shavon Starling Louis, Jessie Light-Wells, Hardy Kim, Jeff Bryan, Daniel Vigilante, Denise Anderson, Andrew Connors, Veronica Cannon, Joel Schultze, Nate Phillips, Jason Santos, and Paul Roberts

*The Church Peeps*, Rev. Bernice Parker-Jones, Santanya Mahoney, Wendy Brown, Natalie Richardson, Carolyn Ellis, Constance Love, Anne Price Collins, Edward Jones, Tony Nixon, LaNita Williams, Faith Presbyterian Church Members, Willie T. Montgomery Jr, Dwight Peace, Katie Murchison Ross, Chauncey Handy, Laura Walters, Tristiana Hinton, Bob Melone, Mount Vernon Presbyterian Church, Gloria Yi, Matt Nabinger, Noelle Castin, Nadia Subaran, Nicole Davis, Yolanda Douthit, and Black Presbyterians United

*Presbyterian Outlook Peeps*, Teri, Jana, Leslie, Jen, Kathy, Jay, Roger, Amy, and George

*Wisdom Wednesday Guests*, Shavon, Jessica, Chris, Zeena, Pat, Teri, and Mika

*Publishing Family Peeps*, Susan, Pavita, Ty, Ebony, Ansari, Hannah

One of the things that inspire me, challenge me, and make me pause is a good quote. I wanted to share with you the voices that I look up, admire, and take their words and activate my own power. Take these quotes, and share. Give them credit. Use it in your preaching, teaching, speaking. May these quotes and phrases give breath, hope, and light.

## CREATING DISTINCTIVE BOOKS
## WITH INTENTIONAL RESULTS

We're a collaborative group of creative masterminds
with a mission to produce high-quality books to position
you for monumental success in the marketplace.

Our professional team of writers, editors, designers,
and marketing strategists work closely together to ensure
that every detail of your book is a clear representation
of the message in your writing.

### Want to know more?
Write to us at info@publishyourgift.com
or call (888) 949-6228

Discover great books, exclusive offers, and more at
## www.PublishYourGift.com

Connect with us on social media

@publishyourgift

Rev. bruce Klunder

- Thy Here Flesh by cole arthur Riley
  - Eclesiastes — Nothing new under
                                    sun
  - Reparation = repair
  - Howard Thurman: Jesus + the interested
  - Standing naked before God
                  Molly Phinney Baskette

Craig amos &
Diana: James II:14-17 Faith/works

Revelation 12:2

Michael 6:8 Linda
maryann: Matthew 7-12
Joon: Go + do likewise
       · Luke 10:37
maryann: Roman 12:15-19
           II corinthian —
                walk by faith not by sight

Blair 1st John: chap4:7

CPSIA information can be obtained
at www.ICGtesting.com
Printed in the USA
JSHW050324130123
36072JS00003B/24

9 781644 844854